DREAMLAND

SHRI
KRISHNA LEELA

Retold by :
T. R. BHANOT

Illustrated by :
N. K. VIKRAM

Conceived by :
VED PRAKASH

DREAMLAND PUBLICATIONS

J-128, KIRTI NAGAR, NEW DELHI - 110 015 (INDIA)

Ph. : 011-2543 5657, 2510 6050 Fax. : 011-2543 8283
E-mail : dreamland@vsnl.com
www.dreamlandpublications.com

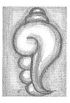

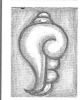

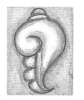

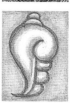

Published in 2012 by
DREAMLAND PUBLICATIONS
J-128, Kirti Nagar, New Delhi - 110 015 (India)
Tel : 011-2510 6050, Fax : 011-2543 8283
E-mail : dreamland@vsnl.com, www.dreamlandpublications.com
ISBN 81-7301-551-1

Printed by

E I H LIMITED
A member of The Oberoi Group
UNIT PRINTING PRESS

PREFACE

Lord Krishna, is considered sacred to Hindu religion. This edition of Shri Krishna Leela throws insight into Lord Krishna's early days, childhood pranks, his adventures, his heroic and victorious deeds.

The unmistakable moral values brought out in this book depicts saving of the human race, by bringing them out from oppression, punish the evil souls for their misdeeds, and depiction of courage and display of super natural powers of the Lord have been depicted in a simple language, for easy assimilation of stories for our young readers.

To make the stories even more interesting, illustrations have been incorporated to make the story reading immensely enjoyable and create an everlasting impression for the reader.

—**PUBLISHERS**

ABOUT SHRI KRISHNA LEELA

Yada yada hi dharmasya glanirbhavati Bharata, Abhyutthanamdharmasya tadatmanam srijamyaham;
Paritranaya sadhunam vinashaya cha dushkritam, Dharmasansthapanarthaya sambhavami yuge yuge.

*Whenever there is decline of righteousness and unrighteousness gets the upper hand, I embody myself forth as a human-being to destroy **evil** and to re-establish **virtue** on the surface of the earth.*

The book—**Shri Krishna Leela**—traces the life story of Lord Krishna as depicted in the 10th canto of the *Shrimad Bhaagwat*. Lord Krishna is worshipped as the incarnation of Lord Vishnu by millions throughout the world. The bewitching personality of the Lord had the irresistible force to captivate even the most irreligious souls of his time. Evidently, the regular reading of this small volume is sure to do away with all evil thinking and kindle a torch of *divine awakening* in the mind of the reader.

In short, the story of Lord Krishna is full of such divine miracles that nobody can help acting upon the ideals mentioned in this book and take to the path of virtue unconsciously. I hope that the readers will try their level best to reap the fullest advantage of this fact by going through this volume page by page regularly to be *one* with the Lord and achieve *salvation*.

— T.R.BHANOT

CONTENTS

1. KANSA WARNED BY A HEAVENLY VOICE

Whenever Satanic values come to prevail on the earth and righteous values decline, the Supreme Being embodies Himself forth as a human being in order to uproot vice and to establish virtue so that the earth may get rid of sinners. The birth of Lord Krishna, thousands of years ago, can be cited as an example to prove this fact. He is the incarnation of Lord Vishnu Himself.

Mother Earth, at that time, was suffering from the tortures of demoniac powers that were at their hey-day. The pitch darkness of sin was devouring noble values. Mother Earth approached Lord Brahma, the creator of the world. So, Lord Brahma escorted her to Lord Vishnu to ask for His help. The Lord consoled her saying, "Don't worry, Goddess Earth ! I myself shall come in the form of Krishna in order to rid you from the clutches of sinners."

The story begins when Kansa, son of Ugrasena, the ruler of Mathura, was escorting his cousin Devaki and her husband Vasudeva to their home just after their marriage. On the way, Kansa was startled to hear a divine voice, **"O cruel king ! the eighth son of this very cousin of yours will be your killer."**

2. DEVAKI AND VASUDEVA IMPRISONED

Kansa felt worried and at the same time he flew into a rage. Though his love for his cousin Devaki was immense, he made up his mind to kill Devaki instantly.

Kansa drew out his sword and thundered, "I will put an end to Devaki's life. Where from, then, will my murderer be born ? There can't be any fruit without a tree."

Vasudeva requested Kansa with folded hands, "Friend ! what are you up to ? Devaki is your cousin. You want the divine prophecy not to come true. So, I give you a solemn word to hand each and every baby over to you as soon as it is born to us." Kansa agreed and said, "All right ! I will not kill Devaki, but I must keep you imprisoned here at Mathura. I won't let you go to your own place."

They returned to Mathura. Kansa took them prisoners in his palace. He also imprisoned his old father, King Ugrasen, seized the throne and declared himself as the king of Mathura. He was sure that his father, if allowed to continue as king, would not let him kill the babies born to Devaki.

3. DEVAKI'S SIX SONS SLAIN BY KANSA

In due course, Devaki gave birth to her first son. Vasudeva sent the message of the arrival of the new born baby to Kansa who sent for Vasudeva along with the baby. Vasudeva complied with the orders. Kansa was pleased and returned the baby to him. Vasudeva came back to the prison happy and satisfied.

After almost an hour or so, Kansa reached the prison. He was almost mad with rage and ill-advised by someone, he had taken a firm decision to kill each baby born to his cousin Devaki. So, he snatched the baby from Devaki and threw the baby on the stone. The baby was killed instantaneously.

Kansa put five more sons of Devaki to death one by one. So, Rohini, the second wife of Vasudeva, left Mathura out of fear and began to live at Gokul. Devaki was again in the family way for her seventh issue. Miraculously, her pregnancy got transferred to Rohini and she gave birth to a son named Balarama.

In course of time, Devaki was to deliver her eighth son. She was extremely worried. Vasudeva consoled her saying that it was this baby who was destined to put an end to the atrocities of Kansa.

Kansa was waiting for the birth of Devaki's seventh baby. But when informed by the royal physician that Devaki was normal, perhaps due to miscarriage, he burst into a peal of laughter and said, "Doctor ! you see, even the would-be babies have started disappearing out of fear from me."

Kansa got the information that Devaki was going to be the mother of her eighth baby. Though boasting of his prowess apparently, in his heart of hearts he was alarmed at the news. So, he called in two hefty guards, one of whom was named Pradyot. Kansa told him, "Mind you ! Devaki is expecting again

and she will soon deliver her eighth issue. You know very well that this baby is considered to be my would-be killer. So, it is imperative that security of the prison should be tightened. I order you to place demons as guards around the jail." I don't want the baby to escape from my clutches.

Pradyot replied, "As you order, sir." Pradyot went away along with his companion and set about making the security of the prison as foolproof as possible.

5. THE BIRTH OF LORD KRISHNA

It was the month of August *(Bhadrapada)* and the eighth night of the waning moon. Devaki and Vasudeva, fettered in chains, were sitting in their prison-room lost in worry. Suddenly, clouds began to thunder and lightning flashed. Through an open window of the prison entered a dazzling beam of light and a fascinating voice resounded, "Devaki ! I am Vishnu. I am going to be born to you shortly." Then the voice addressed Vasudeva, "Take me to Nand Baba, chief of Gokul, as soon as I am born. A daughter will be born to his wife. Bring the girl and put her into Devaki's lap."

Vasudeva and Devaki folded their hands and began to praise the Lord. Just at midnight Lord Krishna was born. The baby was extremely handsome and lovely. It seemed as if it had been smiling on seeing them.

As soon as Vasudeva thought of carrying the baby to Nand Baba at Gokul, his fetters loosened. When he got ready to go, the gates opened and all the guards went into deep slumber snoring heavily. Vasudeva came out unnoticed and advanced on the path leading to Gokul.

When Vasudeva reached the bank of the Yamuna, it began to rain in torrents. Vasudeva was worried. He did not know that Sheshnaga was following him with his hood spread wide over the baby to protect it from the downpour.

Before long, the Yamuna was also flooded. But Vasudeva was determined to reach Gokul with his new-born baby. So, he went on and on and made for the other bank gradually. Inspite of the strong current of water, he proceeded forward without looking back. At one stage, the water of the Yamuna surged upwards with a vengeance but after touching Lord Krishna's feet which he had hung down the basket, it receded to its normal flow.

Once across, Vasudeva soon reached Gokul and made for Nand Baba's house taking help from whoever met him on the way.

Nand Baba was an old friend of Vasudeva. He was highly amazed to see Vasudeva there with a baby in such a stormy weather.

Nand Baba said to Vasudeva, "You have come over to me at this time. How did you get out of the prison ? I am highly pleased to see you here. What can I do for you, my friend ?"

Narrating the entire story, Vasudeva said, "Friend ! I have come over to you at the instance of Lord Vishnu Himself. Here is my eighth baby, Krishna." Then handing the baby across to Nand Baba, he again said, "You have got to bring up this baby of mine as I want to save him from the wrath of merciless Kansa."

Nand Baba replied assuringly, "Vasudeva ! don't worry at all. I will take care of your son even at the cost of my life."

Nand Baba took Krishna inside and put him by the side of his wife, Yashoda. Picking up his own daughter, he brought it out and handed it over to Vasudeva who hastened back to Mathura. Once inside the prison, the gates closed and his fetters were in place again.

As soon as Vasudeva settled down, the guards woke up to be alert on their duty. Not only this, even the baby-girl began to weep as if she had been born just then.

The chief guard of the prison ran to king Kansa. Kansa was beside himself with joy and said, "After all Devaki has delivered her eighth baby. I will go to the prison and put it to death in no time." Kansa reached the prison-room before long and thundered, "Devaki ! hand this baby over to me ; I won't let it remain alive."

"But friend ! she is a girl. What will you gain by killing it ? I request you to spare her life," remarked Vasudeva.

"Shut up ! Give it to me even if it is a girl." Saying these words, Kansa snatched the infant girl from Devaki's hands and tried to strike it on a stone. But the girl slipped out of his hand and flew upwards. While going up, she shouted, "O sinful Kansa ! I am a divine illusion. Your would-be killer has been born and he is the eighth son of Devaki." As soon as Kansa heard these words, disappointment overwhelmed him.

In Gokul, the news of a son born to Nand Baba spread all over the village. People began to flock to congratulate Nand Baba and his wife Yashoda. Whoever came near the baby, could not help gazing at his face fixedly. Young dames were really lost to themselves seeing the baby. The loveliness of infant Krishna, in fact, cast a spell on whoever chanced to see him.

One of the ladies said, "Friends ! Yashoda's lovely son is so charming that I feel like remaining by his side all the time."

Another lady said, "His charm is really fascinating."

"It seems as if Lord Vishnu Himself has come in the shape of Yashoda's son," remarked a third woman. Nand Baba gave cows, corn, clothes and ornaments in charity to the brahmanas, musicians and singers.

Small boys and girls brought toys in the form of presents for the new-born. Some very innocent children went to the extent of saying, "Little one ! grow up soon ; we will take you with us to play."

Kansa did not want to take any chance. He sent for a wicked she-demon named Pootana and ordered her, "Kill all the babies born in Mathura and Gokul in August month. My killer is one of these babies."

Pootna transformed herself into a beautiful dame and began to roam in Mathura with a view to locate the new-born babies born in August. She applied poison on her breasts and suckled every new-born. In this way, she put several babies to death. Then she came to know of the baby born to Yashoda. She went to her house and started talking to her lovingly.

Pootana took Yashoda into confidence and lifted infant Krishna into her arms. She said, "How lovely your baby is ! Isn't he ? When was he born ?"

A lady present there said, "He is Nand Baba's son Krishna. He was born on the eighth night of the waning moon during the month of August."

Pootana's eyes sparkled with hope. But concealing her evil design, she said, "May I fondle him for a while ?"

11. WICKED POOTANA KILLED

Seeing Pootana's affection for Krishna, Yashoda could not refuse. So, Pootana took Krishna into her lap and began to fondle him. Giving Yashoda a slip, she slipped away to a lonely corner and began to suckle him. Little did she know that instead of killing Krishna, she would herself be killed by him.

Young Krishna sucked Pootana's breast with such a force that Pootana felt immense pain and dropped down dead.

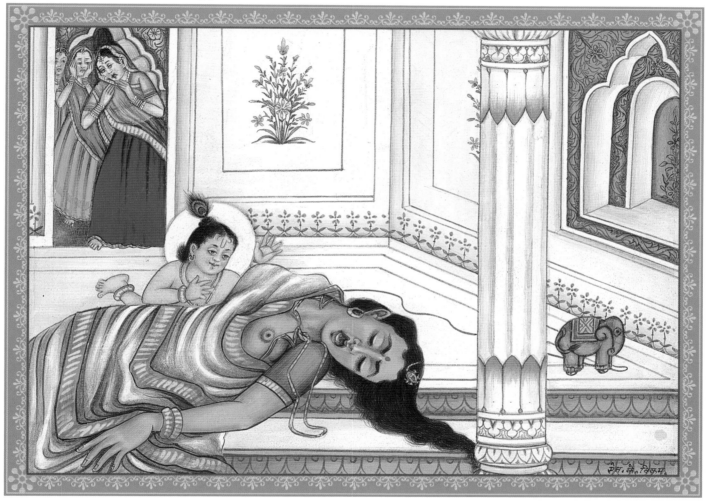

Yashoda came out to look for her son. A number of other ladies also joined her in this search. Soon they reached the spot where Pootana was lying lifeless and Krishna lay smiling by her side.

Yashoda gave out a loud cry out of fear as she had already heard of Pootana's wicked way of killing the infants. Advancing forward, she weaned her son away with a jerk.

The news of Pootana's death spread like wildfire in the entire Gokul and people flocked to see her dead body. They began to praise Krishna. Kansa was shocked to hear of Pootana's death at the hands of Krishna.

12. KRISHNA'S CHILDHOOD EXPLOITS

A brief spell of peace followed Pootana's death. Boys and girls of Gokul were always talking about Krishna who had become the talk of entire Vraj.

One day Yashoda put Krishna to sleep on a baby-cot placed under a hand-cart. A number of pots full of butter and curd were lying on the cart. When Krishna woke up, he felt very hungry and began to exert his arms and legs weeping continuously to attract his mother's attention. He pushed the cart so hard with his foot that it got overturned and all the pots broke into pieces spilling milk, butter and curd.

Kansa was convinced by now that the baby who had killed Pootna, was his would-be killer. So, he thought of another plan to get Krishna killed.

Kansa called a demon named Trinavart and said to him, "Trinavart ! go and kill Krishna in whatever manner you can."

The demon proceeded to Gokul. At Nand Baba's house, he saw Yashoda was sitting with Krishna in her lap. He exercised his miraculous power and she felt her son too heavy to lift. So, she laid him on the ground and went inside to do some household chore. Trinavart carried Krishna away.

Trinavart, a fearful demon, used his miraculous power and caused a heavy dust-storm to blow over Gokul. So, a thick haze prevailed. Then the demon seated Krishna on his shoulders. Young Krishna gripped his neck tightly.

Trinavart flew about hither and thither giving harsh jerks to his body so that Krishna might fall down and be killed. But Krishna didn't loosen his grip till the demon got tired and gave up his attempt to kill Krishna.

Krishna began to grow heavier and heavier. Trinavart tried his best to throw away Krishna from his shoulders but could not. Krishna began to strangulate him and the demon felt his end to be near.

Before long, Trinavart dropped dead on the ground. As soon as he died, the dust-storm caused by him also subsided.

When Yashoda, accompanied by other ladies reached the spot, she was extremely amazed to see her son lying beside the huge demon smiling and sucking his thumb. Yashoda lifted him up and hugged him affectionately.

Now Krishna had grown up a little. He had started walking. So, he used to play with other children of his age in front of his house. One day it so happened that Krishna, while playing, put some soil into his mouth. One of his play-mates went up to Yashoda and told her about what Krishna had done.

Yashoda caught Krishna by the hand and brought him inside. She told him, "My son! it is bad to put soil into the mouth. It leads to worms in the belly and soil-eating children often fall ill. Have you eaten soil, my dear child ? Open your mouth and show it to me."

"No, mother ! I haven't eaten soil at all," replied Krishna and he opened his mouth wide.

Yashoda was wonder-struck to see the entire universe—the sun, the moon, the stars, the earth, etc.—inside Krishna's mouth. Yashoda was now fully convinced that her son was not an ordinary boy but God Himself. Seeing Yashoda amazed, Krishna with his miraculous power made her forget about this episode. Yashoda began to fondle him with deep affection and Krishna began to smile.

15. KRISHNA'S CHILDHOOD PRANKS

Krishna and Balarama used to play in the compound of Nand Baba's house. Yashoda and Rohini felt extremely happy to see them playing. Krishna was in the habit of feeling resented over trifles but even his resentment was very captivating. The dames vied with one another to replenish his mood.

Sometimes Krishna would get angry at meal time. He would insist on eating from Nand Baba's plate. His father would try his best to please Krishna forgetting about his own meal.

At times, Yashoda would feel fed up with her son's pranks and pull up a long face. Krishna would attempt to make her happy using many methods. She would ultimately forgive Krishna for his pranks and hug him affectionately.

Little Krishna's lovely pranks used to fascinate his parents a lot. His lovely handsome captivating looks had cast a spell on the young girls of Gokul and they had started calling him by the name **Manmohan.** Each and every lady in Gokul had a keen desire to see Manmohan in her house enjoying butter, yoghurt, etc. They vied with one another in adorning young Krishna with their personal ornaments.

Krishna as a young child was very active and full of mischief by nature. Now and then, he would be up to some mischief or the other. Indeed it was because of this mischievous nature that his childhood was so charming and fascinating.

Yashoda was always worried for her son due to two reasons. One was that he constantly thought of creating some prank or the other at an appropriate occasion by playing carelessly. Secondly, she feared that he could be taken away by Kansa's men to Mathura.

Whenever Yashoda tried to advise Krishna, he would very cleverly involve her in his innocent talk. As soon as Yashoda turned her attention to some household chore, he would slip away from the scene. She would keep calling out "Kanhaiya ! Kanhaiya !!" helplessly till he returned. She felt satisfied only when some lady of the neighbourhood would bring him to her catching him by the arm.

When anyone came with a complaint against Krishna saying," 'Look Yashoda ! your son has broken my pots full of butter and spilt it on the ground," Krishna would slip away from the scene as soon as possible.

17. KRISHNA, THE BUTTER-THIEF

Krishna had grown up a little more and his mischiefs had also enlarged in proportion. He would sneak into any house along with his friends, break the pots full of butter and curd with a rod and the company would enjoy all of it.

One day a milk-maid saw Krishna and his friends stealing butter from her house. She ran to Yashoda and complained to her saying, "Can't you advise your son ? Come with me and see how he has broken my pots full of butter and yoghurt and spilt everything in the soil."

Yashoda replied helplessly, "What should I do, sister ? I am really fed up with his pranks. I have advised him hard many a time but he does not care for anything. Now it is up to you only to preserve your things carefully."

The milk-maid went away and alerted all the other milk-maids as well. Each of them tried her best to protect her milk and milk-products from Krishna and his mates but it was of no use. Teasing the milk-maids by laying hands on their milk and butter had become Krishna's second nature indeed.

Performance of Indra-yagyas had been a practice in Vraj. These yagyas were performed to thank Lord Indra for timely rains. Gokul was also preparing for one such yagya. So, Yashoda sent all her maids to make preparations for it. She herself sat down churning curd. Just then Krishna woke up and insisted on having a suckle from her.

Yashoda, leaving her job of churning, began to suckle her son. All of a sudden, the milk on the fire-place boiled and began to spill out of the kettle. Yashoda, leaving Krishna, ran towards the fire-place. Krishna was still hungry. So, he got angry and struck the churning pot with a piece of stone. The pot was broken and all the yoghurt was spilt on the ground. Then, Krishna went to the store-room where butter was stored. Getting onto a big mortar, he brought down a pot full of butter and began to distribute it among his friends and some monkeys that were also present there.

When Yashoda came back she saw the mess and got enraged. But Krishna was not to be seen anywhere. With a stick in her hand, she reached the place, where her son was feeding his friends and monkeys with butter.

Krishna got down from the mortar and rushed out followed by his mother. At last when he got tired, he stopped running and began to weep bitterly. Yashoda could not stand the sight of her weeping son and threw away her stick. She caught Krishna by the hand and said, "My dear ! you have become extremely naughty. I must punish you today."

Yashoda brought Krishna inside the house and started tying him to the mortar but the rope fell short. Now Yashoda tried a longer rope but it fell short too. She tried several ropes, each longer than the previous one, but all of them failed to do the job.

Not knowing what to do, Yashoda sat down weeping and said, "Krishna ! why do you trouble me so much ? I won't speak to you at all."

Finding his mother helpless and troubled at heart, Krishna began to smile and tied himself to the mortar with his own hands. Yashoda set about doing some household chore. Krishna sat down on his knees and caused the mortar to tumble down so that it could roll when drawn. Now he began to crawl on his knees towards the twin trees standing in front of the house.

The twin trees were, in fact, the two sons of Kubera—the god of wealth. Their names were Nal Kuber and Manigreeva. It was because of a curse that they had been turned into trees. The story goes that once these two brothers, after taking wine, were having their bath in the company of their wives. All of a sudden, Sage Narada happened to come there. Seeing him, both the ladies put on their clothes and got aside. But both the brothers kept standing naked. Enraged at this, the sage uttered a curse on them," Go and stand as trees in Gokul for ever."

The wives requested the sage to pardon their husbands. When relented, the sage said, "This curse will end when Lord Vishnu appears in Gokul as Krishna."

To keep the word given by Sage Narada to the wives of the two brothers, Krishna dragged the mortar in between the trees. The mortar got stuck up between them. When Krishna exerted force, the trees got uprooted. Falling down, they changed into their real forms. With folded hands, they began to praise Krishna and after seeking his permission, they returned to their place. Nand Baba and Yashoda came there and untied their son. They fondled him affectionately.

One day a fruit-selling lady passed hawking before Nand Baba's house. Krishna heard and went to her with a handful of rice for buying fruit. A child as he was, all the rice got scattered on the ground through his fingers. The fruit-seller was fascinated by Krishna's innocence and gave him a lot of fruit. She went away without taking anything in exchange for the fruit. When the fruit-seller reached home, she was highly astonished to see her basket full of valuable jewels.

Almost every day, some such miracle occurred in Gokul. So, the people of the village felt amazed and at the same time frightened. They apprehended some calamity to overtake them because of these miracles.

Whenever the residents of Gokul complained to Nand Baba and Yashoda about Krishna's miracles, they also felt highly concerned. They would advise Krishna not to do jobs that was beyond his capabilities. However, Krishna would simply laugh the matter away.

The falling of the trees had created panic amongst the villagers. They believed this happening to be the handiwork of demons. So, they held a meeting and decided to leave Gokul and settle at Vrindavan.

Consequently, the people of Gokul packed their belongings and loaded them on their bullock-carts and proceeded to Vrindavan. Women, old men and children were made to sit on the carts while men armed with sticks, swords, bows and arrows walked surrounding the carts on all sides. On one cart Rohini, Yashoda, Balarama and Krishna travelled.

At Vrindavan, the cow-boys used to take their cattle to the pastures for grazing. As Krishna had grown up a little more, he also insisted on going with the cow-boys in order to graze his father's cows. But Nand Baba would not allow him to do so for fear of some untoward happening.

Krishna, however, persuaded Nand Baba to permit him to accompany the cow-boys. His joy knew no bounds when he succeeded in convincing Nand Baba.

The cow-boys were so happy to know that Krishna would be accompanying them. They felicitated him on having got the permission. Krishna's popularity among his friends rested on his mischievous pranks. Early in the morning, his mates would come to his house and call him out for play. Krishna would accompany them and all of them would play together.

Their most favourite game was hide-and-seek. At times, Krishna would disappear from a place where there was nothing to hide behind. All his friends would feel surprised and would start searching him out. When they were unsuccessful, they suspected that he might have been abducted by Kansa's men. So, they would call out his name aloud out of worry.

Seeing his friends worried for him, Krishna would appear smiling from behind them and again run forward calling out, 'Catch me! catch me!!'' The confused friends would again follow him but only to find him missing again.

Tired of searching Krishna, his friends would sit under some fruit-tree. Krishna would drop a ripe fruit from above and say, "Here I am." Balarama would smile at his pranks from a distance as he knew the secrets of his brother's naughty moves.

At Mathura, Kansa was not able to sleep in peace fearing Krishna's magical powers. Trinavart's death had deprived him of his peace of mind indeed. He felt death staring at him. So, he sent another demon to kill Krishna. This demon could transform himself into any creature.

The demon came to Vrindavan in the form of a calf and mingled with Krishna's cows and calves. But Krishna lost no time to spot him through his keen insight. He alerted his brother, Balarama, and all the other cow-boys against the demon—**Vatsasura.**

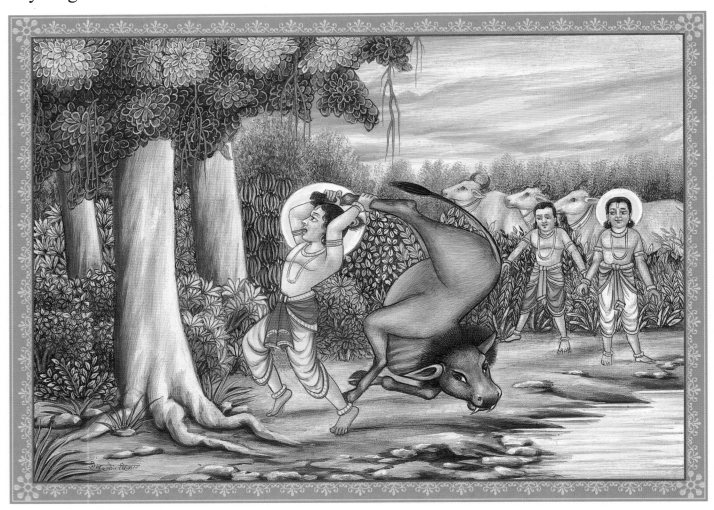

Before Vatsasura could do anything, Krishna went near him slowly, caught him by the hind legs and threw him upwards. After striking against a nearby tree, Vatsasura fell down on the ground with a thud and was killed.

All the cowboys were so pleased at Krishna's exploit that they began to dance merrily.

25. VAKASURA DONE TO DEATH

Vatsasura's death gave a shocked Kansa. So, he sent for Pootana's brother Vakasura and incited him to avenge his sister's death by killing Krishna.

Pootana's brother transformed himself into a huge crane and flew to Vrindavan. He was looking for an opportunity to attack and kill Krishna in order to avenge his sister's death. After sometime, he came to the pool where the cowboys of Vrindavan brought the cattle for a drink.

When the cowboys came to the pool, they were highly amazed as well as frightened to see the huge crane. Some of them ran to Krishna. He immediately knew that it was a demon. As Krishna advanced towards **Vakasura,** he lifted Krishna in his beak.

Krishna began to emit flames from his body and Vakasura had to open his beak. Krishna fell on the ground. Now he started attacking Krishna with his beak.

But Krishna was more than a match for the wicked demon. He tore his beak apart. Vakasura gave out a loud painful scream and dropped dead on the ground.

Hearing of Vakasura's murder, Kansa felt the ground slipping from under his feet. He immediately sent for Vyomasura, son of Mayasura, the chief of demons, and entrusted to him the task of killing Krishna.

Vyomasura left immediately for Vrindavan. Taking stock of the situation carefully, he transformed himself into a cowboy and joined the company of Krishna's friends. After winning their confidence, he suggested a game to be played.

In this game, most of the cowboys were to act as sheep and a few as their guards. Vyomasura was to act as a thief to steal the sheep away. He took away the sheep-cowboys and shut them in a cave. He also carried away some guard-cowboys.

When only four or five cowboys were left behind, Krishna became doubtful. He followed the demon stealthily. He saw through the demon's game and fell upon him. Vyomasura came to his real form and a fierce combat followed. Krishna gave him such a terrible blow that he fell down lifeless. Krishna, then, set all the cowboys free and they all returned to the pasture.

Kansa had become fully aware of the prowess of Krishna by now. But he was still not ready to give up his evil ways. He approached Vyomasura's younger brother Aghasura who promised to kill Krishna. He changed himself into a huge python and lay on the path along which Krishna and his friends drove their cattle daily.

The cowboys, ignorant of the python, kept driving their cattle and were soon inside the wide-open mouth of the huge reptile. They had, in fact, taken it for a crack in a hill. Moreover, they were now careless as Krishna's indomitable strength had made them quite confident.

When Krishna saw the wide-open mouth of the python, he called out, "Friends ! stop short and turn back. You are advancing into the mouth of a python." But the cowboys did not hear his call and went on moving further.

So, Krishna ran fast and he too got into the python's mouth. He began to enlarge his size so that the python might not close its mouth and devour all of them.

Aghasura now found it difficult even to breathe. Before long, he was choked to death and all the cowboys came out safe and sound along with their cattle.

To come out safely out of Aghasura's mouth was no less than coming out of the jaws of death. All the cowboys were very happy and grateful to Krishna. They drove their cattle to the bank of the Yamuna and left them to graze there.

Now the cowboys planned to make Krishna sit in the centre and surround him to enjoy their food. They washed their hands and sat under a shady tree. Some of them placed their meals on leaves while others on stones. Some of them placed their food on the grass while some held it in their hands.

In order to express their gratitude to Krishna, they formed a plate out of wild flowers and placed his food on it.

Now the cowboys began to eat the food sharing it among themselves. Each cowboy tried to put something into Krishna's mouth with his own hands. Krishna was beside himself with joy to see the immense love of his friends for him. So, he gladly accepted whatever each of them offered him.

29. BRAHMA TESTS KRISHNA'S POWER

By now, Lord Brahma, the creator, had been convinced of Krishna's divine power. But seeing him sharing food with cowboys in the forest, doubts prevailed upon him. So, he decided to test Krishna's divine power.

Lord Brahma caused all the cowboys including Krishna to sleep and then drove all their cattle to a cave and shut them inside it. When the cowboys got up, they found their cattle missing. So, Krishna went in search of the cattle.

Now Brahma carried the cowboys to the same cave and shut them too. Having failed to locate the cattle, Krishna came back and found the cowboys missing. So, he used his divine sight and smiled to see through Lord Brahma's trick.

As a counter-move, Krishna, created the duplicates of all the cowboys and animals. So, they kept coming and going just as before. When Lord Brahma checked the cave, he found the cowboys and the cattle shut there. But when he came to the pasture, each grazing cattle and each cowboy disappeared in the form of Lord Vishnu. Lord Brahma came to realize his mistake and approached Krishna with folded hands. Convinced of Krishna's divine power, Lord Brahma could not but let off all the cowboys and their cattle.

30. DHENUKASURA MEETS WITH HIS END

Krishna and his friends went on with their grazing trips as usual for a number of days. No untoward incident occurred.

One day the cowboys suggested to Krishna to go to an orchard to eat fruit. Krishna immediately agreed to go with them. So, all the cowboys, along with Balarama and Krishna, made for the orchard.

Near the orchard lived a demon named Dhenukasura. He used to roam about in the form of a huge ass and kill the animals and people who passed that way.

Reaching the orchard, the cowboys thought of climbing up the trees to enjoy the fruit. First of all, Balarama climbed up a tree and began to shake its branches.

Dhenukasura came running and attacked Balarama. Krishna ran to help his brother. Dhenuka's men also reached there and a severe clash took place. Krishna and Balarama caught **Dhenukasura** and his supporters by the legs and struck them against tree-trunks killing them one by one then and there. After this, the cowboys enjoyed the fruit to their hearts' content and began to dance and sing to celebrate their victory over Dhenuka, the demon.

31. PLAYFUL KRISHNA AND HIS FRIENDS

Krishna used to indulge in various playful activities along with his friends. To hop like frogs, to try to fly like birds, to frisk like deer, to dance as peacocks, to roar like lions and to copy the cries of various birds and animals were some of these activities.

The cowboys had intense love and devotion for their friend Krishna. They used to make garlands of multi-coloured wild flowers for him and put them round his neck. Not only this, they used to adorn him in various ways with a view to winning his favour.

How strange it was that the cowboys could enjoy the close company of Lord Vishnu ! Everybody felt envious of them and wanted to emulate them. How favourite of lady luck these rustic cowboys were indeed !

To accompany the cowboys for grazing his cattle was the daily routine of Krishna now. The cows and the calves kept grazing while Krishna, along with his friends, indulged in various playful activities.

One day when Krishna was busy playing with his friends, their cattle strayed to a distant dense forest. Roaming there, they lost the way and began to low aloud to attract the attention of the cowboys.

Hearing the loud cries of the cattle, the cowboys were startled and they went about looking for them. Soon they reached the forest and found their cattle roaming about among tall grasses.

Unfortunately, the grass burst into flames due to a jungle-fire just at that moment and the cowboys felt worried about the safety of their cattle. They all requested Krishna to do something.

Krishna smiled and asked his friends to close their eyes for a while. The cowboys felt amazed at first but when asked again they complied with Krishna's suggestion and closed their eyes.

When the cowboys closed their eyes, Krishna began to swallow the flames of the fire. When they opened their eyes, there was no sign of fire anywhere.

33. KRISHNA CRUSHES KALIYA

River Yamuna had a deep pit close to its bank where it flowed by Vrindavan. There lived an extremely poisonous cobra along with its family in this pit. This cobra had several hoods and it had poisoned the water of the Yamuna near the pit spitting poison into it.

One day the cowboys chanced to drive their cattle near that pit for a drink. As soon as the cattle drank the water, most of them lay dead. Some cowboys also met with the same fate. So, Krishna decided to kill the cobra. While playing near that pit, Krishna threw his ball into the pit purposely. To get it, he jumped into the pit. Kaliya, as the cobra was popularly called, got furious. Hissing violently, it gripped Krishna in its coil and caused him to swoon. The cowboys raised a hue and cry. The entire village of Vrindavan assembled at the bank. Krishna began to enlarge his body's girth and Kaliya's bones began to break. Feeling helpless, he had to leave Krishna free.

Krishna began to dance on the hoods of the cobra. At the same time, he began to play on his flute. His hoods got bruised and he begged to be pardoned. His wives too implored Krishna to pardon him. Krishna agreed and the cobra moved to some other place leaving that pit for ever.

34. BALARAMA KILLS PRALAMBA

The news of Krishna's exploits was reaching Mathura constantly. This news sent a wave of fright among the people. Kansa felt worried and thought of separating Balarama from Krishna to diminish their strength and then kill Krishna. So, he sent a fearful demon, Pralamba by name, to do away with Balarama.

Pralamba was very dreadful to look at. Two of his front teeth projected out of his mouth while his arms were covered with long hair. His red eyes emitted fire and he possessed great miraculous powers.

Transforming into a cowboy, Pralamba mingled with Krishna's friends and suggested to play a game. In this game, the members of the losing side were to carry the members of the winning side on their backs over a certain distance.

Pralamba purposely fell in with the losing side, seated Balarama on his back and ran towards Mathura. When Balarama resisted, he came to his real form. Balarama got extremely furious and gave such a fierce blow on his head that it broke into two. Pralamba fell down dead instantly. When the news reached Kansa, he felt almost broken-hearted, but he was quite helpless and disappointed.

Every new exploit of Krishna endeared him to the people and they were now fully devoted to him. They showered on him much more love than he had enjoyed at Gokul in his infancy. The livestock of Vrindavan also expressed devotion to Krishna as he had helped them out of serious troubles many a time.

The flute was the most favourite musical instrument of Krishna. Its tunes cast such a spell on the people of Vraj that they ran to where Krishna was playing it. When he played on his flute, all the cows and calves came running and surrounded him. Even the birds of the forest came flying and nestled in the nearby trees to enjoy the captivating musical tunes.

As far as the milk-maids of Vrindavan were concerned, the magic of Krishna's flute would make them almost senseless. They used to weave dreams about Krishna. One of these maids was Radha who loved Krishna the most—so much so that she wanted him to live in her heart for ever. Krishna too loved her more than anybody else. At times, other girls of her age tried to tease Radha with keen taunts in the name of Krishna. But she was madly in love with him and so she never took their teasing seriously.

36. KRISHNA ENJOYS DELICIOUS DISHES

One day Krishna accompanied by his mates, went into a deep forest. In due course of time, they felt awfully hungry. But they had no food with them.

The cowboys expressed a desire for eating something to Krishna who himself was hungry. All of a sudden, they felt the sweet smell arising out of a yagya fire. It seemed that a yagya was being performed somewhere near by. Krishna sent some cowboys to bring food from there.

The cowboys saw that some Brahmanas of Mathura were performing the yagya. They asked for food but the Brahmanas scared them away.

Krishna now sent the cowboys to the wives of the Brahmanas for food. When these ladies came to know that Krishna wanted food, they themselves reached the forest with delicious dishes. These dishes had been prepared for the Brahmanas to be eaten after the completion of the yagya. Balarama and Krishna, along with the cowboys enjoyed the tasty dishes heartily.

37. KRISHNA LIFTS THE GOVARDHANA HILL

Since ancient times, Indra has been worshipped for timely rains. When the people of Vrindavan started the preparations for the worship, Krishna called them and said, "Why do you worship Indra ? Worship your cows that give you milk. Worship the Yamuna that gives you water for drinking and irrigation. Worship the Govardhana hill on whose sides our cattle graze."

So, the people of Vrindavan gave up worshipping Indra and began to worship cows, the Yamuna and the Govardhana hill. Indra, the rain-god, felt highly offended and decided to teach the people of Vrindavan a bitter lesson.

Indra let loose torrential rain on Vrindavan and lightning flashed terribly accompanied with deafening thunder. A rain-storm broke out and it began to rain heavily. The people of Vrindavan were frightened and ran to Krishna for help.

Krishna took all of them to the Govardhana hill. He raised the hill on the little finger of his left hand. It served as a big umbrella under which the people and the cattle of Vrindavan took shelter for seven days till Indra accepted his defeat.

Since this incident, people have worshipped the Govardhan hill on the day following the Diwali festival. This festival is celebrated as such even today.

38. INDRA FEELS HUMILIATED

The pride of Indra, the rain-god, had been decimated. He had not been able to do any harm to the people of Vrindavan. Krishna had kept them safe under the Govardhan hill during the week-long torrential rain and violent storm.

Indra had realized his blunder as he had come to know that Krishna was not an ordinary boy but Lord Vishnu Himself. So, riding his heavenly elephant, called Airavat, he came to Vrindavan accompanied by Kamadhenu, the cow known for her capacity to fulfil each and every wish. Reaching there, he begged for Krishna's pardon with folded hands.

Kamadhenu was beside herself with joy because Krishna had saved all the cattle of Vraj. So, she decided to add a new title—**Govind**—to Krishna's name. She requested Krishna to accept this title which means *protector of cows*. She rained her milk on Krishna to give him a bath while Airavat showered the water of the heavenly Ganga on him with its trunk. Thus the title—Govind—came to be duly conferred on Krishna.

Ekadashi (eleventh day of the moon) has great religious importance. Usually a fast is observed on this day. Nand Baba was to observe a fast on Ekadashi during the month of Kartik (November). So, he was to get up early on Dashami (tenth day of the moon) to have a bath in the Yamuna. The night being cloudy, Nand Baba could not judge the time correctly and reached the bank of the Yamuna in the small hours for a bath. An envoy of Varuna, the water-god, was guarding the river at that time. He caught Nand Baba and presented him before his master, the water-god.

When Nand Baba did not return till sunrise, the people of Vrindavan felt worried. They thought their chief had been drowned. A large crowd assembled on the bank of the Yamuna.

Krishna at once plunged into the river and went to the abode of the water-god. Seeing him, the god felt afraid and realized the mistake committed by his envoy. With folded hands, he begged Krishna to pardon him.

Krishna came back to Vrindavan along with Nand Baba. The people were overjoyed to see their chief alive and praised Krishna.

40. RAAS LEELA ENACTED

Krishna's handsome looks and proportionate muscular body was a source of attraction for all the young ladies of Vrindavan. But their love for him was divinely pure and not sensual at all.

Sharad Poornima (full-moon night in November) is a festive night in Vraj. Just at moonrise, Krishna began to play on his flute roaming through the streets. The melodious tunes of the flute cast a spell equally on the girls and the brides.

Unable to control themselves, they came out of their homes, caring little for the social norms. They surrounded Krishna and began to sing and dance.

Lord Krishna urged all the ladies to return to their homes but they flatly refused to do so. So, **Raas Leela** *(Divine Drama)* began to be enacted.

Each milk-maid cherished a desire to get closer to Krishna. Seeing through their pure feelings, he decided to fulfil their wish. He multiplied his form and appeared with each of them. So, each milk-maid felt as if Krishna had been dancing in her company only. The divine dance went on throughout the night.

On Shivaratri night, worship of Lord Shiva is performed five times. Nand Baba started this worship in a temple located in Ambika forest along with all the milkmen and cowboys of his village. Due to the night-long wake, everybody felt sleepy. So, all of them lay down outside the temple and soon fell fast asleep.

After some time, a python came crawling out of the nearby bushes. It began to swallow sleeping Nand Baba from the side of his feet.

Nand Baba woke up and began to shout for help. The noise waked up all the milkmen who began attacking the python with burning torches. Though the python's body got severe burn-injuries all over, yet it did not leave Nand Baba.

Krishna came running there and struck his foot at the python. As soon as Krishna's foot touched the reptile, it changed into Vidyadhar and began to sing the glory of Krishna.

Vidyadhar had been changed into a python after a curse uttered on him. The touch of Krishna's feet rid him of the curse and he returned to his abode.

42. KRISHNA KILLS SHANKHACHOODA

Holi is among the most important festivals of Vraj even today. It was the full-moon Holi night, Krishna, accompanied by his brother Balarama, went to the nearby forest and began to play on his flute. The magical tunes cast a spell on all the animals and birds. Not only this, the young girls and ladies of Vrindavan also ran to where Krishna was playing melodious tunes.

A subordinate of Kubera, the god of wealth, was roaming in the forest. His name was Shankhachooda. Seeing the young beauties, he could not control himself and abducted all of them. The milk-maids shouted for help calling out Krishna and Balarama. Some of them began to weep aloud as well.

Both the brothers ran to where the shouts were coming from. They had uprooted some plants to use against the aggressor. Seeing them giving a hot chase, Shankhachooda took to his heels. Leaving Balarama to take care of the ladies, Krishna followed him and overtook him after a short chase.

Krishna delivered such a fierce blow on Shankhachooda's head that his forehead broke into two and he fell down dead. A jewel came out of his forehead which Krishna presented to his brother.

46

Kansa felt that his death at the hands of Krishna was getting more and more imminent. So, he chalked out another plan to put an end to Krishna's life.

Kansa entrusted a demon, named Arishta, with the job of eliminating Krishna. Arishtasura reached Vrindavan and began to create trouble there. He wanted that his activities should force Krishna for an encounter.

Arishtasura transformed himself into a violent bull and damaged many a house with his horns. He uprooted several trees and killed a number of cows and calves too. So, Krishna decided to punish him.

Krishna and Balarama went to where the demon was creating trouble. Krishna challenged him. Balarama, when he saw the furious bull, asked Krishna not to face him but Krishna paid no heed to his advice.

Mad with rage to hear Krishna's challenge, Arishtasura rushed towards Krishna who caught hold of his horns and pushed him back to a distance. Then he got onto his back with a sudden move, and giving no chance to the demon to do anything, Krishna twisted his neck with such a force that he fell down dead.

Now Kansa was trembling with fear at the very thought of Krishna. He had been fully aware that his end was quite nearing.

He deputed Keshi, a very strong demon, to put an end to Krishna's life. This demon used to roam in the form of a dark black horse, very dreadful to look at, so much so that even gods feared to see eye to eye with him.

Keshi came to Vrindavan at Kansa's instance in the form stated above. He started running through the streets of the village neighing furiously. Scared people shut their doors and the cattle broke loose to run for safety. Krishna lost no time to know that he was a demon sent by his maternal uncle, Kansa. So, with a view to chastising him, he challenged Keshi who was on the look-out for an opportunity for an encounter with Krishna.

Keshi fell upon Krishna in full fury. He opened his mouth to bite Krishna who pushed his arm into his mouth and broke all his teeth. He enlarged the length and girth of his arm to such an extent that Keshi's throat got choked and his belly got inflated. Finally, it burst causing the demon to fall down dead on the ground.

Keshi's death disheartened Kansa and he could not think of any warrior who could undertake the task of putting Krishna to death. So, he decided to take recourse to treachery to kill his nephew—Krishna.

Akroor, the chief of the charity department of Kansa, was a very saintly person. Kansa asked him to go to Vrindavan and bring Nand Baba's family and other respectable milkmen to participate in the *Bow-Yagya*. Being a godly person, Akroor gladly agreed to go to Vrindavan. He had a keen desire to see Krishna, the incarnate of Lord Vishnu.

Reaching the outskirts of Vrindavan, Akroor caught sight of Krishna's foot-prints and his heart began to bubble with joy and devotion for Krishna. Stopping the chariot, he got down and paid obeisance to them. He felt proud of being lucky enough to have a chance to do this religious act.

Akroor, then reached Nand Baba's house and delivered Kansa's message to him. Nand Baba entertained him duly. Akroor disclosed everything about Kansa's treacherous plot to kill Krishna.

Nand Baba did not want to take Krishna and Balarama to Mathura with him. But Krishna did not want to lose this opportunity of killing sinful Kansa to rid the Mother Earth of his burden.

Krishna himself got proclaimed the invitation of king Kansa throughout the village. All the milkmen got ready with their carts to visit Mathura. The milkmen loaded their carts with butter, curd and milk to be presented to the king and proceeded towards Mathura. Krishna and Balarama were seated on Akroor's chariot and the procession, led by Nand Baba, got on its way to Mathura.

The milk-maids came running and surrounded Akroor's chariot. They would not allow him to take Krishna and push him into the jaws of danger. Moreover, they feared that Krishna might not come back to Vrindavan.

Akroor tried his level best to advise the milk-maids but they were not ready to listen to him. The very thought of separation from their darling Krishna haunted them like a nightmare. They caught the wheels of Akroor's chariot. At last, they returned when Krishna himself consoled them with his assuring sermon.

Akroor proceeded to Mathura after seating Krishna and Balarama in his chariot. Reaching the bank of the Yamuna, Akroor stopped the chariot. Seeking the consent of both the brothers, he went to have his bath in the river.

When Akroor had his very first dip in the river, he saw Krishna and Balarama inside the water. But when he drew his head out of the water, he found both the brothers sitting in the chariot. He felt highly amazed.

Now Akroor had a second dip. He saw Lord Vishnu relaxing on the body of Sheshanaga inside the water. He found that Krishna's face closely resembled that of Lord Vishnu.

Akroor felt elated to have a glimpse of Lord Vishnu in the river-water. Having taken his bath, he said his prayer and returned to the chariot. Time and again, he was looking at Krishna with eyes full of devotion. He was thanking his stars to be lucky enough to act as the charioteer of Krishna. He was more than convinced that Krishna was Lord Vishnu Himself.

48. KRISHNA PUNISHES THE WASHERMAN

Nand Baba and the other milkmen had reached Mathura much earlier than Akroor and both the brothers. Nand Baba had set up a camp in a garden outside the town. When Akroor reached there, Krishna and Balarama got down from the chariot while Akroor advanced further. Reaching the court, he informed the king of the arrival of Nand Baba's group and then made for his home.

Krishna and Balarama had their meals and rested for some time in the garden. Then they sought Nand Baba's permission and went sight-seeing round the town of Mathura along with their team of cowboys.

Roaming about, they came across the royal washerman who was going to the palace to deliver the washed clothes. Krishna said to the washerman jokingly, "Washerman ! give us some of these clothes to wear." Proud of his being in the royal service, the washerman snubbed Krishna and Balarama using disgraceful and abusive words. Krishna could not tolerate the insult and decided to teach him a lesson.

At first Krishna rebuked the washerman hard. But when he did not give up his rudeness, Krishna gave such a hard blow with the side of his palm on his neck that he fell down dead on the spot. The other washermen took to their heels.

52

49. KRISHNA REWARDS THE TAILOR

The clothes carried by the royal washerman were lying near his dead body. Krishna and Balarama opened the bundles of clothes and asked their companions to put on the beautiful dresses. When the cowboys had done so, they looked funny because the clothes did not fit on them properly.

One cowboy said to the other, "Your clothes are very loose," while the other said, "This shirt is very tight for you." So, they took off the clothes and threw them away. A tailor, sitting near by, was seeing all this.

The tailor had been struck with the handsome looks of all the cowboys. So, going up to them, he said, "May I mend these clothes so as to fit on each of you nicely ?" Then without waiting for the answer, he set about mending the clothes. In a short time, he did the job and now the clothes looked very nice on them.

Krishna was very pleased with the tailor and conferred on him the boon of becoming a noble godly person. The tailor felt very pleased and thanked his stars.

You must have heard of Sudama, fast friend and class-mate of Krishna at guru Sandipani's gurukula. There was a royal gardener with this very name in Mathura. He was very noble, humble and polite.

After conferring a boon on the tailor, Krishna along with Balarama and other cowboys went to the house of the royal gardener named Sudama. The gardener had heard of the exploits of Krishna.

Seeing Krishna present there, the gardener was beside himself with joy. He greeted Krishna and his friends and duly entertained them.

Then the gardener prepared beautiful garlands and presented them to all the cowboys. As for Krishna and Balarama, he garlanded them with his own hands. Krishna was extremely happy at the gardener and he conferred the same boon on him as he had done on the tailor. The gardener felt flattered at the boon and said, "I am so lucky to have this opportunity indeed."

These words pleased Krishna all the more and so he said, "Prosper day by day ; that is another boon for you."

51. KRISHNA BREAKS THE YAGYA-BOW

Now Krishna made up his mind to go to the site of the Bow-Yagya. They enquired about this site from the people and advanced in that direction.

Reaching the site of the yagya, Krishna and Balarama looked at the bow which was very heavy—so much that even Kansa could lift it with difficulty after worshipping it daily. He had deputed Balarama brave soldiers to guard the bow.

Pushing the soldiers aside, Krishna and Balarama went near the bow. Krishna at once lifted it and drew its string with such a force that it broke into two with a loud twang.

Seeing this, the soldiers fell upon the brothers who beat them with the pieces of the bow. They ran to Kansa and told him all that had happened. Kansa got furious and he despatched a regiment of armed soldiers along with an elephant to deal with Krishna and Balarama. But they eliminated the entire regiment and the elephant in no time.

Krishna and Balarama returned to the camp and related to Nand Baba the entire incident. Then having had their bath, they took their meals and went to sleep.

Next day, Kansa invited Krishna and Balarama to see the bouts among his wrestlers. Before their arrival, Kansa got his most dangerous tusker— Kublayapeed—intoxicated with wine and posted it at the gate of the wrestling-arena along with its *mahout*.

This was done to incite the intoxicated elephant to attack Krishna and Balarama as soon as they reached the gate of the arena. Kansa was sure that the beast would certainly trample both the brothers to death.

As soon as both the brothers turned up, the mahout incited the elephant and it fell upon them. It curled its trunk round Krishna's body and tried to lift him up. Despite its best efforts it could not be successful.

Krishna and Balarama broke both its tusks and the beast screamed in pain. Krishna caught hold of its trunk and flung it on the ground. Then both the brothers beat it to death with its own tusks.

The mahout too was given a sound beating and he too succumbed to the thrashing. The people standing around took to their heels out of immense fear.

53. THE WRESTLING BOUTS

Kansa had pinned great hopes on his tusker–Kublayapeed. But the fearful end of the beast crashed all his hopes. So, he asked his famous wrestlers, Mushtik and Chanur, to challenge both the brothers for bouts.

Krishna and Balarama went inside the arena to see the wrestling bouts. Chanur and Mushtik challenged them for bouts. So, They took off their clothes, and entered the arena. Both the wrestlers were using deceptive moves to checkmate the brothers but all in vain.

Kansa's wrestlers did not aim at free and fair wrestling. Their objective was to kill both the brothers who were well on their guard. Each unfair move on the part of the wrestlers was rendered useless by them.

When Chanur got extremely tired, Krishna lifted him well above his head and flung him onto the ground with a great force. Instantly he was killed.

Chanur's death did away with Mushtik's courage and he too was killed by Balarama. Some others–Koot, Shala, Toshal, etc.—also met with the same fate.

Having seen his strongest wrestlers being killed before his own eyes, Kansa began to tremble. At the same time, he flew into a rage and ordered all the playing drums and bugles to be silent. Then he shouted to his soldiers, "What are you seeing now ? Catch hold of these two boys and do away with them."

Not only this, Kansa asked his soldiers to put Nand Baba, Vasudeva and Ugrasena along with all the milkmen to death as well.

How could Krishna tolerate such punishment for Nand Baba and his dear ones ? He challenged Kansa and jumped on the dais where he was sitting. Kansa trembled all over in fright and tried to escape. But Krishna held him by the hair and flung him on the ground with a jerk. Then Krishna sat on his chest and began to rain blows on his ribs. Kansa cried for help, "Save me ! Save me !" He implored Krishna to spare his life. He could see his death staring before him. Krishna then strangled him to death.

Seeing their brother being killed, all the eight brothers of Kansa fell upon Krishna and Balarama who did away with all of them too, one by one.

Krishna and Balarama now made for the prison-room where Devaki and Vasudeva were imprisoned. Struck with fear, the guards opened the gates of the prison-room at once.

Both the brothers went inside and untied the fetters of Vasudeva and Devaki. The parents kept gazing at their sons with tearful eyes. How handsome, captivating and well-built they looked indeed ! Devaki and Vasudeva hugged them closely.

Then Krishna and Balarama escorted them to the site of yagya where a large crowd of people had assembled to raise slogans in Krishna's admiration, "Glory be to Krishna ! Glory be to Balarama!"

Praising both the brothers for their courage and bravery, the crowd greeted them and their parents with profound respect and devotion. Not only this, they also raised slogans condemning wicked Kansa as well.

Krishna pacified the crowd and asked for their opinions on the enthronement of someone on Kansa's throne. It was decided that the old King Ugrasena (Kansa's father) was the rightful king of Mathura.

Respecting the public opinion, Krishna decided to set Ugrasena free. Both the brothers went to the prison where the old king had been put behind the bars. They untied his chains and he was given a bath and dressed in a royal robe. Then escorting him to the court, Krishna and Balarama seated him on the throne and placed his usurped crown on his head.

People started raising slogans of glory to Ugrasena and Krishna and of condemnating Kansa. King Ugrasena embraced Krishna and Balarama and showered blessings on them. Seeing this, all the courtiers too began to admire both the brothers.

A large number of noble persons had fled from Mathura and settled at other places because of Kansa's excesses. Now that Kansa was no more, these people returned to their respective homes in Mathura.

King Ugrasena began to rule as before taking due care of his people and observing all religious norms essential for an ideal king. As a result, people became fearless, prosperous and happy again. So, they began to fulfil their duties towards the state.

57. SACRED-THREAD CEREMONY

Now Krishna bade farewell to Nand Baba and other milkmen of Vrindavan after giving them valuable gifts and showering due honours on them.

Vasudeva chalked out a programme to make his sons step into *Brahmacharya ashram* duly according to the religious rites. A yagya was held and sacred–thread ceremony of both the brothers was observed. Rohini had been called to Mathura to participate in all these religious rites.

With clean-shaven heads, vermilion marks on their foreheads, mekhalas and loin clothes on their waists and plasha rods in their hand, both the brothers looked very impressive indeed.

Vasudeva, Devaki and Rohini were beside themselves with joy to see their sons through the ceremony. They were extremely overjoyed and happy.

The sacred-thread ceremony having been over, Vasudeva decided to send his sons to some gurukula for education. After thinking thoroughly, they were sent to Sage Sandipani's ashram located at Ujjain.

Both the brothers threw themselves heart and soul into studies. They served their teacher with devotion and he, in turn, was very happy with them.

There were a number of other students too at the gurukula. One of them was Sudama, son of a poor Brahmana. Krishna was very close to him. In course of time, they became bosom friends.

One day, the wife of Sage Sandipani asked Krishna to go to the forest and fetch dry wood for the havan. Krishna, accompanied by his close friend, Sudama, went to the forest to collect and bring dry wood.

As soon as both the friends were ready to leave the forest with wood, a violent storm began to blow. It went on for a long time and both the friends lost their way. They roamed hither and thither along with the faggot of wood. The sun set and darkness prevailed all around. So, they were forced to pass the night under a tree.

Next morning, the sage came to look for them. Seeing them with the wood, he felt very pleased at their obedience and showered blessings on them.

59. KRISHNA PAYS GURUDAKSHINA

Krishna and Balarama, being divine beings, were themselves a store-house of knowledge. Their going to the gurukala aimed at establishing ideals for others and at highlighting the honour of the teacher in the society. In a short period of sixty-four days, they mastered the Vedas, the Upavedas, other religious books and all the arts.

Sage Sandipani was amazed at the grasping power of both the brothers. His inner vision guided him to undertsand that Krishna was an incarnation of Lord Vishnu. So, he viewed Krishna with great devotion.

Having finished their schooling, Krishna and Balarama took leave of Sage Sandipani and offered to pay gurudakshina. The sage said, "I want my son, who was drowned in the river while bathing some time back, to be alive."

Krishna went to the abode of death-god and asked him to bring the sage's son to the earth to live with his parents. The sage was so pleased to have his son back. Then Krishna and Balarama took leave of their school-mates and returned to Mathura.

Each of Krishna's miracles had a big secret behind it. Kalayavana was a tyrant person who was a terror to the people. Let us read how Sri Krishna eliminated him in a dramatic way.

Kansa's father-in-law Jarasandha was a very powerful king. He was enraged at the murder of his son-in-law and attacked Mathura seventeen times. Every time, his army was routed by Krishna and Balarama.

Kalayavana raised a large army and incited by Jarasandha planned to attack Mathura. Krishna had got a new city-Dwaraka built on a peninsula on the western coast of India. He sent the people of Mathura to live there in safety.

Kalayavana followed Krishna like a shadow. Krishna left Dwaraka unarmed and bare-footed.

Kalayavana too left his chariot and ran after Krishna to catch him and kill him. Krishna ran on and on with Kalayavana following him at his heels. Having covered a long distance, both of them came to the mouth of a cave.

61. MUCHUKUND PRAISES KRISHNA'S GLORY

Running on and on, Krishna led Kalayavana into a cave where a king named Muchukund was sleeping soundly because of a boon conferred on him by the gods. Krishna lay his yellow shawl on the sleeping king and hid himself aside.

Kalayavana too came inside the cave. In the heat of his rage, he mistook the sleeping king for Krishna and struck him hard with his foot. Muchukund was disturbed and he got up. As soon as he cast an angry look at Kalayavana, he was burnt alive to death.

The story goes that Muchukund had fought a war against the demons to save the gods. The gods were very pleased and they asked him to ask for a boon.

Muchukund, weary of a long war, asked for a long sleep. So, the gods said, "Go and sleep at any place on the earth. Whoever disturbs you during your sleep, will be burnt alive as soon as you look at him."

Krishna had led Kalayavana into the cave to have him burnt alive and to prove the veracity of the boon that the gods had conferred on King Muchukund. How difficult it is to perceive the miracles performed by Krishna !

King Muchukund saluted Krishna with profound devotion and praised him a lot. Then seeking his permission, the king proceeded to the forest for meditation.

As soon as Krishna got out of the cave, Kalayavana's army barred his way. Balarama had also reached there by now. So, both the brothers put Kalayavana's army to rout and proceeded to Dwaraka.

Jarasandha, who had already suffered defeat seventeen times at Krishna's hands attacked Mathura once more. But knowing that the people of Mathura had shifted to Dwaraka, he directed his army to march towards Dwaraka.

Krishna and Balarama, who were coming to Dwaraka after routing Kalayavana's army, were overtaken by Jarasandha. Seeing the large army, Krishna, under a dramatic move, fled the place along with his brother Balarama. Because of this miraculous move, Krishna came to be known as **Ranachhor** also. This word means—*runner from the battle-field.*

63. RUKMINI CARRIED OFF BY KRISHNA

Rukmini, daughter of King Bhishmaka of Vidarbha, had fallen in love with Krishna. So, her father decided to marry her off to Krishna. But Rukmi, her brother, was against this marriage. He wanted her to marry Shishupal.

The old King Bhishmaka had to agree to what his son Rukmi wanted. So, he sent a message to Shishupal to come with a marriage-party. As for Rukmini, she also sent a secret letter to Krishna to come and save her. So, Krishna had reached Vidarbha earlier than Shishupal with the marriage-party. Balarama too followed Krishna with a large army.

A few hours before the marriage ceremony, Rukmini came out of the palace for worship of Mother Goddess in a temple. Krishna seated her in his chariot and made for Dwaraka.

Shishupal and Rukmi followed Krishna with their armies but Balarama barred them on the way and defeated their armies.

Krishna, on reaching Dwaraka, duly married Rukmini according to the religious rites. Before long, Balarama too returned to Dwaraka.

A powerful noble, named Satrajit, lived in Dwaraka. He had worshipped the Sun–god and got a divine jewel from him. Satrajit was very proud of this jewel. Krishna had once or twice asked the noble for the jewel but he refused.

One day Prasenajit, Satrajit's brother, went for a game in a nearby forest. He had taken the jewel with him. There he had to confront a lion and was killed along with his horse. As Prasenajit did not return, Satrajit blamed Krishna for his murder. Krishna proceeded to the forest to bring the reality to light.

In the forest he found the dead bodies of Prasenajit and his horse. Also, he saw a lion lying dead. He spotted some foot-prints leading into a nearby cave.

Jambavan, who had killed the lion and taken away the jewel, lived in that cave. Krishna asked Jambavan to hand the jewel over to him. On his refusal, a combat followed and went on for 28 days.

Finally, Jambavan accepted his defeat and returned the jewel to Krishna. Also he gave his daughter Jambavati to him in marriage. Krishna handed the jewel over to Satrajit who too, gave his daughter, Satyabhama, to Krishna.

Nagnajit, the ruler of Kosala, had reared seven huge bulls. When his daughter, Satya, came of marriageable age, he declared, "Whoever puts a common string into the noses of the seven ferocious bulls, will become my son-in-law."

A number of princes came to try their luck but none could do the feat. Each of them went back having been wounded and defeated. Now the king felt very sad as the feat seemed quite impossible to perform. At last Krishna reached Kosala and offered to do the feat.

Krishna did not take long to string the noses of all the seven bulls together. The king was beside himself with joy. So, he gave his daughter to Krishna in marriage.

Now Krishna had eight queens. Four of them were Rukmini, Satyabhama, Jambavati and Satya about whom we have already read.

Before them, Kalindi had herself chosen Krishna as her husband, while Mitravinda was won in a swayamvar. Bhadra's father had offered his daughter to Krishna and Lakshmana was also won in a swayamvar.

Narakasura was a fierce demon. He was a tyrant who had abducted and imprisoned sixteen thousand princesses.

Not only this, he had snatched the *ear-rings* of Aditi, the mother of Indra, the famed umbrella of Varuna, the water-god, and the Jewel Hill (Mani Parvat) from the gods.

The gods were very frightened of this fierce demon. So, they went to Lord Indra and requested him to do something to do away with the fearful demon. Finding the job much too difficult, Indra further implored Krishna for help.

So, Krishna mounted Garuda along with his queen Satyabhama and went to Narakasura's capital. Using his magical powers, the demon had raised a wall of high hills around the city and also fortified his capital with fire-flames, a deep moat full of water and a coat of poisoned air. Also, he had fixed automatic missiles and laid magical traps at every step.

Krishna pierced through all these barriers and challenged the demon for a battle where in he was killed. Krishna now rescued all the sixteen thousand princesses from the prison. Then he enthroned the demon's son as the next ruler.

Along with the rescue of sixteen thousand princesses, Krishna had also got back the ear-rings of Aditi, canopy of the water-god and the Jewel Hill of the gods. Krishna went to Indra and returned these things–each to its master. When Krishna was about to leave, Satyabhama insisted on having the *Kalpataru* for herself. Kalpataru is known for its capacity to fulfil every desire of man. Krishna uprooted the tree and handed it over to his queen. Indra could not tolerate it. He at once called all the gods and held a meeting. They all branded Krishna's action as improper and attacked him.

A fierce battle followed which resulted in a defeat for the gods who ran pell-mell to save their lives. So, Indra was at his wit's end. Feeling ashamed, Indra fell on Krishna's feet and begged to be pardoned.

Indra implored, "This tree is a heavenly tree. Be kind enough to keep it at Dwaraka only till you yourself are there and then return it to us."

Krishna agreed to what Indra had said. Coming to Dwaraka, he planted the tree in the compound of Satyabhama's palace.

Banasura was a ferocious demon who had one thousand arms. He had an extremely charming daughter who chanced to see Anirudh, the grandson of Krishna, and fell in love with him. So, she sent Chitralekha, one of her close friends to bring Anirudh to her using her miraculous power. Chitralekha did the job for her friend.

When Banasura came to know of it, he used the Nagapasha and bound him and took him captive. Sage Narada came to know of it and he informed Krishna of the mishap. Krishna collected a large army and marched towards the capital city of Banasura and attacked on all sides. Banasura was a devotee of Lord Shiva and so the Lord came to help the demon along with his pupils. Krishna killed all the soldiers of the demon and also the pupils of Lord Shiva. As for Shiva, he used *Jarimbhak*, a sleep-prevailing weapon, on him and he was lost in deep slumber.

Now Krishna began to cut off the arms of Banasura and he raised a hue and cry which aroused Lord Shiva from his deep slumber. On Shiva's request Krishna spared the last four arms of the demon who now gladly gave his daughter to Anirudh in marriage.

69. NRIGA REDEEMED FROM A CURSE

Much earlier than Krishna's time, there had been a highly charitable king named Nriga. He gave innumerable cows in charity to Brahmanas and came to earn the title-*Charity King*.

Once he committed a blunder, though quite unknowingly. He gave in charity a cow which he had already given in alms to a Brahmana. The Brahmana got very angry and uttered a curse on Nriga, "Be a chameleon and keep lying in a dry well for ever." The curse came to have its effect on the king.

The well in which the chameleon lived was near Dwaraka. One day some boys of Krishna's family, while playing, came near this well. One of them chanced to peep into the well. Seeing the chameleon, he told his companions about it.

The boys felt amazed to see the huge chameleon and began trying to get it out of the well. Having failed to do so, they went to Krishna and asked for his help. Krishna came to the well and drew out the reptile with his hand. As soon as Krishna's hand touched the chameleon, it got transformed into Nriga again. The curse had lost its effect indeed. Nriga praised Krishna and seeking his permission proceeded to heaven.

We have read that Krishna, having been invited by Kansa to Mathura, had come there to take part in the Bow-Yagya along with Nand Baba and other respectable milkmen of Vrindavan. After killing his maternal uncle, Kansa, and his wrestlers, Chanur and Mustik, he had set Vasudeva and Devaki free and also enthroned his grandfather, Ugrasena, restoring his lost crown to him.

Then Krishna and Balarama went to the gurukula of Sage Sandipani at Ujjain and completed their schooling within a short period of 64 days only. Also, he had constructed the town of Dwaraka at a peninsula bordering the west coast of India. Soon after this, he did away with Kalayavana, Narakasura, Banasura and several other evil persons. Not only this, he had salvaged King Muchukund and King Nriga also.

Paundraka, the ruler of Chunar, raised his head as he was very jealous of Krishna's rise. Incited by his flatterers, he declared himself to be the incarnation of Lord Vishnu. As people considered Krishna to be the human form of Lord Vishnu, Paundraka challenged Krishna for a combat. When they came face to face with each other, Krishna saw through his two artificial arms and other accessories often seen in the hands of Lord Vishnu. Krishna defeated him and put him to death along with his supporter, the ruler of Kashi.

The murder of the ruler of Kashi enraged his son Sudakshana. He made up his mind to avenge his father's death. So, he invoked Lord Shiva and asked him for a boon that could enable him to kill Krishna.

Lord Shiva suggested to him to perform a yagya known as the *Killer-Yagya*. The Lord further said that the killing power produced out of the yagya could kill anybody who was not devoted to the Brahmans.

Sudakshana performed the above named yagya and created the killing power known as **Kritya.** Then he sent it to Dwaraka aiming at Krishna and Balarama to be killed. Little did the foolish fellow know that Krishna was an embodiment of Brahmanhood. So, Kritya could not harm him in any way.

As soon as Kritya reached Dwaraka, Krishna perceived it through his divine insight and shot his **Chakra** at it. Unable to face the chakra, Kritya turned about and ran back to where it had come from. Reaching Kashi, it made short work of Sudakshana and also the Brahmans who had performed the yagya.

Shortly afterwards, Krishna's chakra reached the town of Kashi and reduced the whole of it to ruins.

Jarasandha, the ruler of Magadha, was Kansa's father-in-law. He had attacked Mathura seventeen times but every time suffered a crushing defeat. Even then, his power had not been broken and he was ready for a trial of strength once again.

Yudhishtira, the Pandava king, was planning to perform a *Rajasuya Yagya* to celebrate his victories over most of the kings of North India. Krishna apprehended trouble at the hands of Jarasandha during the performance of the yagya. He advised Yudhishtira to do away with him before the yagya.

Krishna's advice appealed to Yudhishtira's mind and he sent his brothers, Arjuna and Bhima, with Krishna to the capital of Magadha. Reaching there, Bhima challenged Jarasandha for a wrestling bout. The wrestling bout went on for thirteen days, but without a win for either of the contestants.

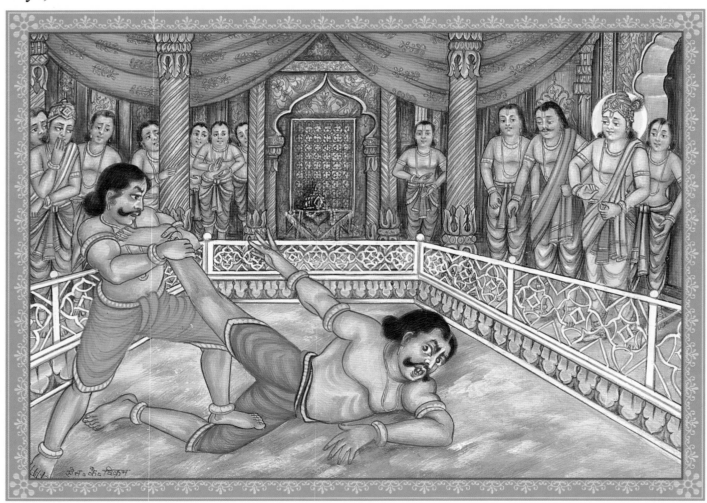

On the fourteenth day, Krishna signalled Bhima to tear his opponent into two halves demonstrating the action by tearing a leaf and throwing its two parts into opposite directions. Bhima followed the signal and acted up to it literally. As a result, Jarasandha was killed.

73. KRISHNA WASHES THE FEET OF THE BRAHMANAS

Jarasandha had imprisoned eighty-five kings without any reasons. All these kings were set free after the death of Jarasandha. They were sent back to their respective capitals and at the same time invited to take part in the yagya to be performed by Yudhishtira.

Not only this, Sahadev, son of Jarasandha, was coronated to succeed his father as the next ruler of Magadha.

After Krishna returned to Indraprastha, capital of Yudhishtira, the yagya was started. All the near relatives were entrusted with important jobs, viz, acceptance of presents was handled by Duryodhana, the job of giving alms was given to Karna, preparation of eatables was put under Bhima while Krishna undertook the humblest of the jobs–washing the feet of the Brahmanas and the sages coming to participate in the yagya.

The arrangement of the yagya was so efficient that everyone was happy and satisfied. The most remarkable thing about the yagya was that the Brahmanas and the sages were beside themselves with joy to have the divine touch of Krishna's hands on their feet.

The Rajasuya Yagya was nearing its completion. The last rite was to confer honours upon the kings who had participated in the ritual. Before starting this rite, it was customary to worship the best participant according to the manner prescribed in the religious scriptures.

Yudhishtira did not want to choose the best candidate for worship after his own will. So, he decided to consult all the participants present there. Sahadev, ruler of Magadha, proposed the name of Krishna as he was obliged to him for his coronation. Most of the kings and the Brahmanas approved the proposal, though a number of kings opposed it also. The opposing faction consisted of the supporters of Shishupal, who had an old grudge against Krishna because of Rukmini.

Shishupal opposed the worship of Krishna as the best participant using objectionable and disgraceful words for him. He suggested that either Bhishma or Drona should be the candidate for worship. But these two elderly participants had already supported Krishna's candidature. So, a wrangle cropped up over the point and Yudhishtira was at a loss to understand what to do.

The brawl over the choice of the rightful candidate for worship was not coming to an end as Shishupal and his supporters were dead against the worship of Krishna. At last Krishna stood up and addressed the gathering, "I beg the attention of all of you to what I am going to say. Shishupal is my cousin—son of my father's sister. I would have done away with him far earlier, but for his mother's request to pardon him. Now I warn him to come to the right path. I won't say or do anything till he has used one hundred disgraceful terms for me. But after that, I won't spare him at all."

Better sense did not prevail on Shishupal and he went on with his abusive words against Krishna. So, Krishna flew into a violent rage and declared, "The fellow is bent upon meeting with his end and I am helpless." Saying so, Krishna wielded his *chakra* and directed it at Shishupal. It went revolving to Shishupal and severed his neck from the rest of his body. Then it returned to Krishna's hand. Everybody present was frightened to look at Krishna who had assumed his divine colossal form (virat roopa). Everybody stood up and prayed to Krishna to be cool. So, he came to his normal form and resumed his loveable look as before.

Shalva was a close friend of Shishupal. Having got the news of Shishupal's death, he was mad with rage and made up his mind to avenge his friend's death. He invoked Lord Shiva and asked for a boon. When the Lord gave his assent, Shalva asked for a unique vehicle that could move on land, in air and on water with equal agility and at the same time could be invisible when required. Lord Shiva ordered Mayasura, chief of the demons, to build the vehicle for Shalva. Obtaining the vehicle and having his army on board, Shalva marched towards Dwaraka. Krishna was not there as he was still at Indraprastha.

Pradyumna, Krishna's son, faced Shalva with his army and routed a major part of it. The news soon reached Krishna who hastened to Dwaraka to deal with Shalva. Using his famous bow—Sharang Bow—he did away with the remaining soldiers of the invader.

Then Krishna struck the vehicle with his mace and it was broken to pieces. Enraged at it, Shalva sprang at Krishna with a mace in his hands but Krishna was more than a match for him. He directed his chakra at him and it cut off both the arms and the neck of the opponent instantly.

77. DANTAVAKRA PUT TO DEATH

King Dantavakra was the ruler of Karusha kingdom. He was a bosom friend of Shalva. When Dantavakra heard that his friend had marched to Dwaraka with a view to punish Krishna for the murder of Shishupal, he lifted his mace and made for the battle-field to help his friend Shalva.

Dantavakra was so confident and proud of his prowess that he did not take any army with him. Not only this, he forgot to take his chariot even in the heat of his enthusiasm to help his friend to chastise Krishna. Before long, he reached the field where the battle was going on.

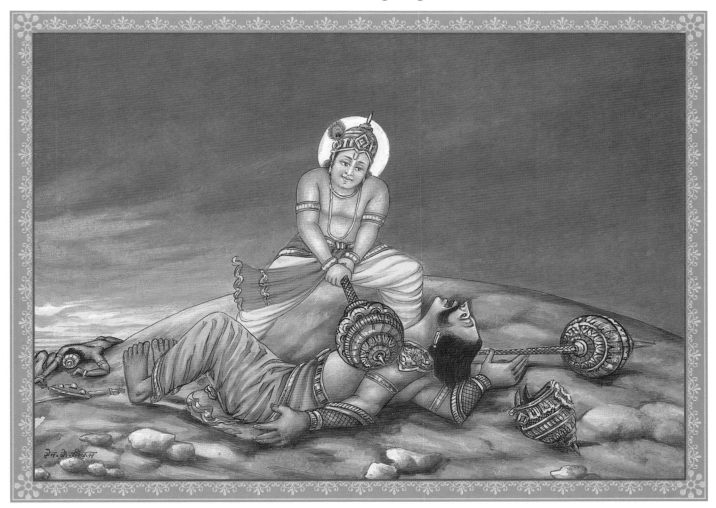

As soon as Dantavakra saw the dead body of his friend Shalva, he became mad with rage and his eyes began to emit fire. Seeing Krishna standing near by, he lifted his mace and struck Krishna on his chest. Krishna was, however, able to bear the brunt of the blow and he challenged Dantavakra to be on his alert. Krishna lifted his mace–*Kaumodaki*–and hit it at the chest of his opponent. Dantavakra could not stand the blow. His chest-ribs were broken and staggering over a few steps, he fell down lifeless on the ground.

Duryodhana was very jealous of the rise of the Pandavas. The constant help that they were getting from Krishna, was an eye-sore to him as well. He chose to checkmate them through some trick. He knew the weakness of Yudhishtira for playing dice. So, he conferred with his maternal uncle, Shakuni, who was an excellent play master in dice-games. When Duryodhana invited Yudhishtira to the game, he could not refuse and soon reached Hastinapur.

Shakuni played on Duryodhana's behalf and through his unfair moves, heaped defeat after defeat on Yudhishtira. Having lost his kingdom and every other belonging, Yudhishtira staked his four brothers. When he had lost them too, he staked himself and thereafter his wife Draupadi as well.

Duryodhana asked his brother Dushasana to bring Draupadi to his court and to strip her. Draupadi was dragged to the court and Dushasana set about stripping her. The helpless queen prayed to Krishna for help. Krishna responded through his miraculous power. The saree of Draupadi got increased to such a length that Dushasana grew tired of drawing it off her body.

Enraged at Duryodhana's vicious attempt, Bhima had pledged to kill Duryodhana and his brother Dushasana. This pledge frightened Duryodhana's father, Dhritrashtra, who returned to Yudhishtira everything he had lost in the game. This embittered Duryodhana and he decided to humble the Pandavas in another way. He asked Yudhishtira to have his lost things on the condition that the Pandavas would go into exile for thirteen years, the last year of which they would remain underground and untraced. Inspite of this, Duryodhana was not satisfied even now. He pleased sage Durvasa through hospitality and then persuaded him to go to the Pandavas along with his ten thousand pupils and ask for meals.

Durvasa complied with Duryodhana's request and went to the Pandavas along with his pupils. Draupadi found it impossible to entertain the sage and apprehended a curse from him. She prayed to Lord Krishna who at once responded. Reaching there, he asked for the akshayapatra which had been given to her by the Sun-god. He touched it and asked Draupadi to go on serving food to the guests. The akshayapatra resumed its capacity and it did not run short of food till all of them were satisfied fully. So, Durvasa felt small and he had to return happy and satisfied.

We have already read about Krishna's class-mate and close friend Sudama. Sudama was very poor. But his wife Sushila often goaded him to go to Krishna and ask for financial help. At last Sudama agreed to visit Dwaraka.

Sushila gave a small packet of parched rice to Sudama to offer as a humble present to Krishna. Reaching Dwaraka, Sudama sent word to Krishna about his arrival. Krishna rushed barefooted to the gate to receive his friend and escorted him inside. Seating him on a cushion, Krishna washed his feet and entertained him duly. Rukmini, Krishna's wife, kept fanning Sudama all this while.

Seeing Krishna's grandeur, Sudama felt very small and could not dare to offer the humble present that he had brought. But Krishna knew everything. He signalled to Rukmini to snatch the packet from Sudama. The royal couple enjoyed the parched rice as if it were a sumptuous dish.

Sudama stayed with his friend for a few days and then returned home. He was highly astonished to see his hut replaced by a magnificent house full of luxuries and comfort and his family dressed in valuable garments.

Soon after Sudama's return to his village, there occurred a solar eclipse. As we know that a fair is held at Kurukshetra on this occasion. Krishna proceeded to Kurukshetra with his parents, Balarama and other Yadava nobles. Here he met Nand Baba, Yashoda and his childhood friends.

During the conversation that took place between the near-and-dear ones, Devaki came to know that Krishna had revived the son of his guru after he had been drowned while bathing at a river near the *gurukula*. So, she insisted on seeing all her six sons killed by Kansa at Mathura. Krishna could not afford to disappoint his mother and soon proceeded to the abode of death-god.

The six dead sons of Devaki were, in fact, sons of Sage Marichi. They had been cursed by Brahma for laughing at him. So, they had been turned to demons as a result of the curse. Krishna went to Bali, chief of the demons, and brought all the six of them to his parents. They were very pleased to see their sons. The effect of the curse also disappeared. They paid obeisance to Devaki, Vasudeva, Balarama and Krishna and went back to their abode.

The Pandavas after passing thirteen years in exile had returned to Indraprastha. They asked Dhritrashtra to return their kingdom. But Duryodhana was not ready to part with what he had been possessing for over thirteen years. So, a war between the two became inevitable. Preparations for the war between the Kauravas and the Pandavas began.

Alliances started to be made on both sides. In the course of these moves, both Arjuna and Duryodhana approached Krishna for help. Incidentally, Krishna was enjoying a sound sleep at that time. Duryodhana was lucky to reach earlier than

Arjuna. So, he sat towards Krishna's head. Arjuna, when he reached, sat near Krishna's feet. When Krishna got up, his eyes first fell on Arjuna because he was just in front of his face. He asked him to narrate the purpose of his visit.

Duryodhana interrupted saying that he had come earlier and the first choice of demanding anything should be given to him. Krishna shook his head and allowed Arjuna to have his say. "Arjuna ! I will help both of you. Choose one thing out of myself and my large army." Arjuna chose Shri Krishna. Duryodhana laughed at his folly and was happy to have Krishna's army.

Yudhishtira, we know, was a sagacious person who hated war though he was a great warrior. He tried his level best to put off the war against Duryodhana but all in vain. As his last effort, he sent Krishna as his envoy to advise Duryodhana to give up the war-path and settle the matter through negotiations.

Just on the eve of Krishna's departure, Draupadi came to him and showing her ruffled locks of hair said, "O Krishna ! you are going with a message of peace to Duryodhana. I request you not to forget about my hair that was drawn and dragged in the open court by Dushasana. I have not dressed these locks for the last thirteen years."

Krishna replied, "O Draupadi ! be consoled. My peace-mission is not going to put the war off because it is inevitable. Rest assured that you will be duly avenged. Nevertheless, my visit to Hastinapur will certainly prove that the Pandavas, on their part, have done their best to avert the war, and thus the entire blame will rest on the shoulders of the Kauravas."

When Krishna went to the Kaurava court, he was accorded a warm welcome. Dhritrashtra entertained Krishna duly and asked him about the purpose of his visit. Krishna talked of averting the war by giving a small territory—five villages–to the Pandavas and thus restoring peace to the entire family. He argued with Duryodhana from every angle on this point in order to convince him that the impending war would be highly disastrous.

Duryodhana was in no mood to reconcile. He said, "No, not at all; no territory, not equal to a needle-point even. I have won their kingdom. It can't be returned until and unless they win it back with the force of their armies. Why should they beg for it like urchins?" When Krishna asked Duryodhana to restrain himself from using disgraceful words for the Pandavas, he flew into a rage and ordered his men to capture Krishna and imprison him.

Hearing Duryodhana's words, Krishna felt upset not out of fear but due to disappointment over the failure of his mission. But he was not ready to take chances because Duryodhana could be wicked to any extent. He decided to show Duryodhana a glimpse of his divine power. He assumed his colossal form. Everybody present there was amazed as well as afraid to see it.

In spite of being offended with Krishna, Duryodhana could do no harm to him because according to the prescribed norm, an envoy could not be harmed or punished even if he used harsh words against the king to whose court he had been sent. As for Krishna, he was so displeased with Duryodhana that he rejected his stately hospitality and left the court at once.

Vidhura, a cousin of Dhritrashtra, was a godly person who knew that Krishna was an incarnation of Lord Vishnu. Having left the court, Krishna went to Vidhura's house where he was received warmly. Vidhura's wife was equallly God-fearing and pious. She was beside herself with joy to see Krishna at her house. Lost in deep emotion and profound devotion, she decided to entertain Krishna with bananas.

How strange ! Vidhura's wife was offering banana-peels to Krishna for eating while the inner fruit was being thrown away into the dust-bin. She was, in fact, lost to herself in devotion and could not pay attention to what she was doing. As for Krishna, he enjoyed the peels as if they were more delicious than the bananas. He did not even point out to her about what she was doing.

Krishna's peace mission had miserably failed and he had returned to Indraprastha to give a green signal for the preparations for the impending war. Both the armies marched to the field of Kurukshetra. Krishna had accepted to act as Arjuna's charioteer only.

As Krishna drove Arjuna's chariot to the no-man's land, Arjuna saw his blood–relations, revered Guru Drona and respectable Bhishma standing in the opposite camp. His mind shook and he was filled with doubts. He said to Krishna, "I won't fight at all. Is it proper and worthy of me to kill all my near-and-dear ones only to get a throne ? No, no; I won't do it at all."

Krishna felt upset when he saw that Arjuna was quite averse to war. It was at this time that Krishna delivered his sermon of the Gita to Arjuna. He said, "O Arjuna ! you have got the right to act only without bothering about the result. Man's soul is immortal and it is only the body that perishes. This is a holy war and a true warrior (*kshatriya*) cannot afford to be a coward." Hearing these words, Arjuna realised his mistake and got ready to fight.

Bhishma loved the Kauravas and the Pandavas alike. Though he was fighting on behalf of Duryodhana, yet he had never tried to kill any of the five Pandavas. He had been killing only their soldiers. Duryodhana did not like it and he said to Bhishma, "Grand-father ! you are avoiding the killing of the Pandavas while fighting. Do you want them to be victorious ? I did not expect such a thing from you as you have always been faithful to the Kaurava throne."

Bhishma had nothing to reply back and so he said, "You will never gain a victory over the Pandavas because you are following an evil plan whereas they are fighting for a just cause."

The next day, Bhishma fought like a lion so much so that he caused Arjuna to swoon when struck by his arrows. The horses of Arjuna's chariot were also killed. How could Krishna tolerate all this ? His anger knew no bounds and he decided to break his pledge. Raising the wheel of a broken chariot, he ran towards Bhishma. Bhishma felt frightened and folded his hands in order to beg his pardon. Seeing this, Arjuna came running, pacified Krishna and taking him by the arm, he took him back to his chariot.

88. KRISHNA SENDS DRAUPADI TO BHISHMA

Incited by Duryodhana, Bhishma once again took a pledge to kill the Pandavas. The news of this pledge reached the Pandava camp and they were extremely worried. They knew that Bhishma had the boon to die only when he wanted to do so and so it was impossible to kill him. Once again, Krishna came to their help and asked them not to feel anxious at all.

Escorting Draupadi to Bhishma's camp at night, Krishna advised her to make obeisance to the old warrior who was meditating with his eyes closed. Draupadi went in and said, "Glory be to you, grandfather !" Without opening his eyes, Bhishma uttered a blessing, "May you never be a widow and enjoy the company of your husband till your death !"

When Bhishma opened his eyes, he was surprised to see Draupadi sitting in front. He at once followed that she had come to him on the advice of Krishna who must be there somewhere around. Just then, Krishna stepped in and Bhishma stood up to greet him with profound devotion and piety. In this way, Krishna had saved the Pandavas from the fatal wrath of Bhishma.

After the fall of Bhishma, Drona assumed the command of the Kaurava army, but he was killed. His son Ashwatthama got very offended with the Pandavas. So, he directed the *Narayanastra* at them. It was a quality of this weapon that it never hit a soldier who was on foot or armless or who had turned his back towards it.

Seeing the dangerous Narayanastra, all the warriors threw their arms and got off their chariots turning their backs towards it.

But Bhima considered it an insult to do all these things. On the other hand, he kept roaring aloud brandishing his mace in the air. The result was that innumerable fire-arrows came out of the above named Narayanastra and shot towards Bhima at a full speed.

When Krishna saw this, he rushed towards Bhima and stood in front of him turning his back towards the Narayanastra. Not only this, he bent Bhima's head down with his hands and hid it in his arms. Also, he snatched his mace and threw it on the ground. As a result, the Narayanastra went back without harming Bhima or any of the Pandavas.

90. KRISHNA SAVES ARJUNA FROM BEING BURNT

The battle of the Mahabharata ended with a defeat for the Kauravas and a glorious victory for the Pandavas. So, Krishna drove Arjuna's chariot back to the Pandava camp and asked him to get down at once. But Arjuna refused saying that conventionally it was the charioteer who would get down first followed by the warrior. But Krishna insisted on Arjuna's getting down from the chariot first. Arjuna could not afford to disobey Krishna and got down along with his bow and quiver of arrows. It was after this that Krishna came down from the chariot.

Arjuna was surprised to see that the chariot along with the horses, was burnt to ashes as soon as Krishna got down from it. He asked Krishna to explain how and why it had happened.

Krishna said, "The chariot was already going to be burnt but I had checked this phenomenon deputing Hanuman on guard. If conventionally I had got down earlier than you did, you would also have been burnt alive along with the chariot and the horses. That was why I insisted on your getting down first. As soon as I got down, Hanuman flew away leaving the chariot unguarded and it was burnt to ashes."

91. KRISHNA SAVES PARIKSHAT

It was the night of the seventeenth day of the battle of Mahabharata. Drona's son, Ashwatthama, had killed five sons of Draupadi in cold blood while they were sleeping. Luckily, Krishna had taken the Pandavas away in order to save them.

When the Pandavas returned the next day, Draupadi told them about the woeful happening. The Pandavas were struck with grief and an enraged Arjuna chased and captured Ashwatthama. He was going to kill him but Draupadi asked him to spare his life. Arjuna got Ashwatthama's head shaven clean, dug the jewel out of his forehead and then set him free.

Enraged at his insult, Ashwatthama shot his divine weapon (*Brahmastra*) at the Pandavas with a view to put an end to their generation. But Lord Krishna had saved them using his divine power. Then the Lord ran towards Uttara who was in the family way. The Brahmastra attacked the infant in Uttara's womb but Krishna saved it too. But the infant got wounded from all sides. So, he was named Parikshat. This very prince was enthroned as the next king by the Pandavas when they proceeded to heaven.

92. LORD KRISHNA PROCEEDS TO HEAVEN

There lived a Brahmana at Dwaraka. Whenever a child was born to him, it died. So, the Brahmana was very grieved. He used to place the dead infant at the royal gate. Seeing the Brahmana in grief, Arjuna gave him a pledge to save his next child. But this time, the infant dramatically disappeared soon after its birth.

Arjuna was highly perturbed to see his pledge broken and so he got ready for self-immolation. Krishna took Arjuna to Lord Narayana who said, "Arjuna ! I wanted to see you along with Krishna. So, this drama of the disappearance of the Brahmana's son was enacted." The Lord returned all the children of the Brahmana to Arjuna who duly handed them over to their father.

Having been offended with the Krishna's family, the local Brahmanas uttered a curse on them, "All of you will die fighting among yourselves." Balarama had already passed away and most of the other members of Krishna's family had also died fighting. One day Krishna was sitting under a *peepal tree* in a forest. Taking his brilliant heel to be the eye of a deer, a hunter shot an arrow at it. As a result, the Lord breathed his last and proceeded to heaven.

33+